Eye To Eye, Heart To Heart

Written by
Pamela Pech

Illustrated by
Joan Zander Millard

Published by Pamela Pech
Reno, Nevada

ISBN: 979-8-9871078-0-5 (hardcover)

Library of Congress Control Number: 2022919160

Published by Pamela Pech
Reno, Nevada
https://www.discoveryofSelf.us

Illustrations by Joan Zander Millard, ZeeeArts
https://www.facebook.com/zeeearts/

Book design by Carolyn Mirelez, Electronic Ink Graphic Design
www.electronicinkaz.com

Book Shepherd Ann Narcisian Videan, ANVidean.com

To Kristi and Noah,
whom I love beyond words and who are absolutely perfect
despite all the imperfect parenting.

To Eva, Jackson, Eden, and William,
my amazing grandchildren, who will each change
the world in their own beautifully unique way.

Acknowledgments & Gratitude

I want to share my deepest expression of gratitude to the following people who helped me in making this book a reality:

To "Ben" and "Jennie"
Whoever you might be, thank you for seeing that something special in Gabbi, saving her life, and enriching ours.

To Gary and to my entire family and extended family
For their loving encouragement and support.

To Dr. Karen Gedney, Lisa Walsh, Jacquin Webb, Robert Reed, Jason Stipp, and Deb Conrad
For contributions assisting me to convey the prison information as accurately and as close to "the real story" as possible.

To Jackie Crawford, Mike Budge, Greg Smith, and Lisa Walsh
For the courage and persistence it took to bring a program such as Pups on Parole into existence.

To Joan Zander Millard, Ann Videan, Kristi Wayland, and Carolyn Mirelez
For putting much love and soul into this project—truly making it our book.

To Dad, Mom, and Anna Scarboro
For making books and reading together a joyful part of my childhood.

To Dr. Karen Gedney, Rhoda Olsen, Anne Studebaker Garlow, and Cynthia James
For the loving and heartfelt testimonials.

To Emilio Parga
For reminding me, "You have a book in you."

To Marilyn Kelly
For sustaining Gabbi's second chance through loving and consistent training, both of Gabbi and especially me.

Gabbi sighed and dropped her head toward the floor of her kennel. *Here I am in this lonely room again,* she thought.

She stood, stretched her legs, turned a complete circle, and plopped herself down in the far corner of the cage. The metal bars pushed into her back but she didn't care. She just wanted to tuck herself into the tightest ball possible and move far away from everyone and everything.

If only she could make herself invisible.

Two words kept echoing in her head.
"Bad dog!"

It certainly must be true, she thought.

Why else would she be back in this
room with so many dogs barking and
whimpering? Their bodies trembled and
she knew their hearts ached with fear.

She understood because
she was scared too. Would she
always be in this room? Would she
ever find a forever home? She groaned and
pushed herself tighter against the kennel bars.

Gabbi had never lived in a real
home, and she longed for one with
all her heart. Her first memories
were of running helter-skelter
through city neighborhoods.

As a pup, she hunted for scraps of food, often knocking over garbage cans to search for a tidbit of anything to fill her tummy.

She didn't recall why or how she came to be on the streets alone, she just remembered being cold and hungry, and people yelling, "Bad dog!" when the cans tipped over.

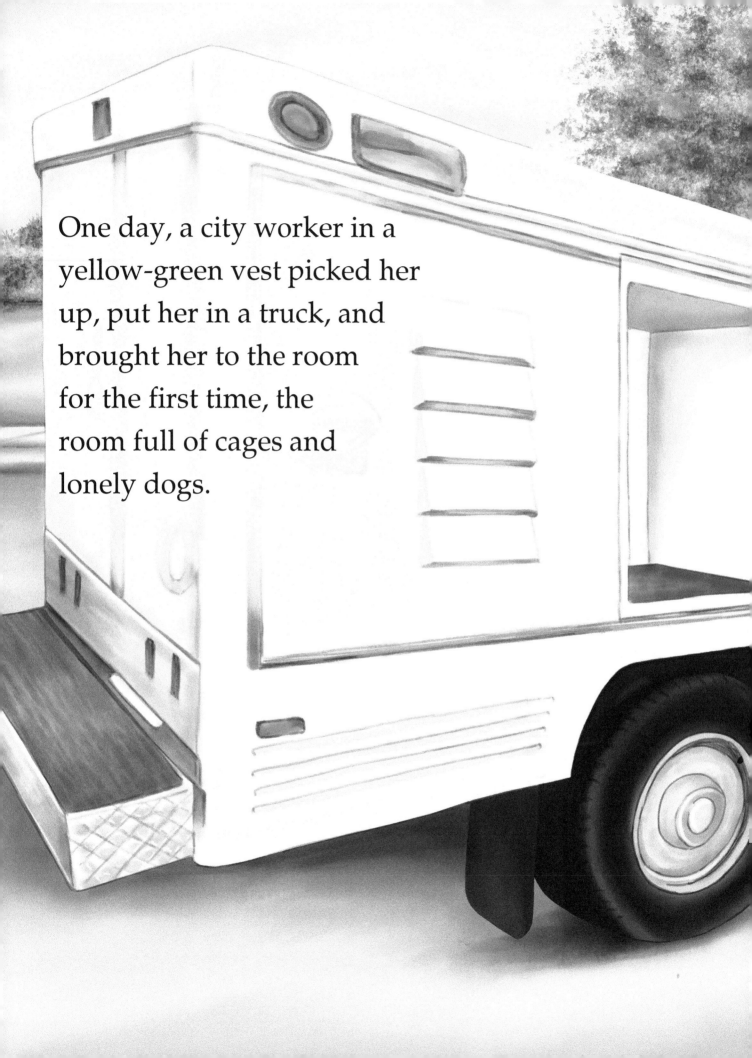

One day, a city worker in a
yellow-green vest picked her
up, put her in a truck, and
brought her to the room
for the first time, the
room full of cages and
lonely dogs.

A man with big muscles adopted her and brought her to his house. When he left her alone for a long time, Gabbi sometimes made messes by the door. Though he was usually kind, her "accidents" made him very angry. He yelled, "Bad dog!" and hit her. It didn't take long for him to decide she wasn't the right dog for him.

Back to the lonely room she went.

Next, a young family adopted her. They wanted a dog for their son, Michael, to have fun with as he grew. But Gabbi was growing bigger, too, every day.

Sometimes she would jump up on Michael as he ran, thinking he wanted her to chase him. That often knocked him down, scaring him and making him cry. He'd then grab her ears and yank her tail. That hurt, so she'd nip at him to make him let go.

Soon Gabbi heard those words again. "Bad dog!"

The family decided Gabbi wasn't the right dog for them so, once again, here she lay in the lonely room.

Of course they brought me back, thought Gabbi. *I keep doing bad things. I'm not the right dog for anyone! I will never have a forever home.*

Over and over, she thought about all the things wrong with her and why she was such a bad dog.

Though Gabbi thought she wanted to be invisible, what she truly longed for was someone to see her for who she really was.

She wanted them to recognize the love she had to give, and for them to love her in return. She hurt inside. It wasn't a pain like when she stepped on a thorn or when someone hit her or pulled her ears. It hurt all the time, like an ache.

Lying, sad and exhausted, in the back corner of her kennel, Gabbi finally fell asleep.

The next morning she awoke to a woman at her kennel door who knelt down to rub her head.

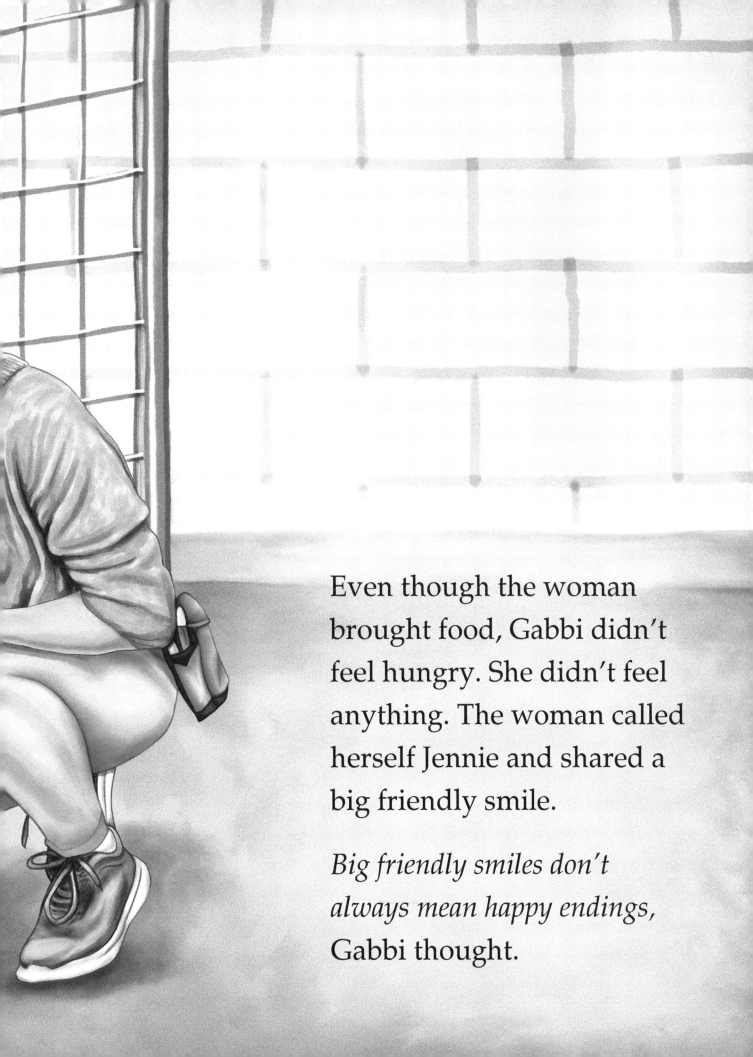

Even though the woman brought food, Gabbi didn't feel hungry. She didn't feel anything. The woman called herself Jennie and shared a big friendly smile.

Big friendly smiles don't always mean happy endings, Gabbi thought.

Something unexpected caught her attention. Without lifting her head, she focused her eyes on a bright yellow object peeking out of Jennie's pocket.

A ball! Suddenly Gabbi realized her tail was wagging for the first time in a long time.

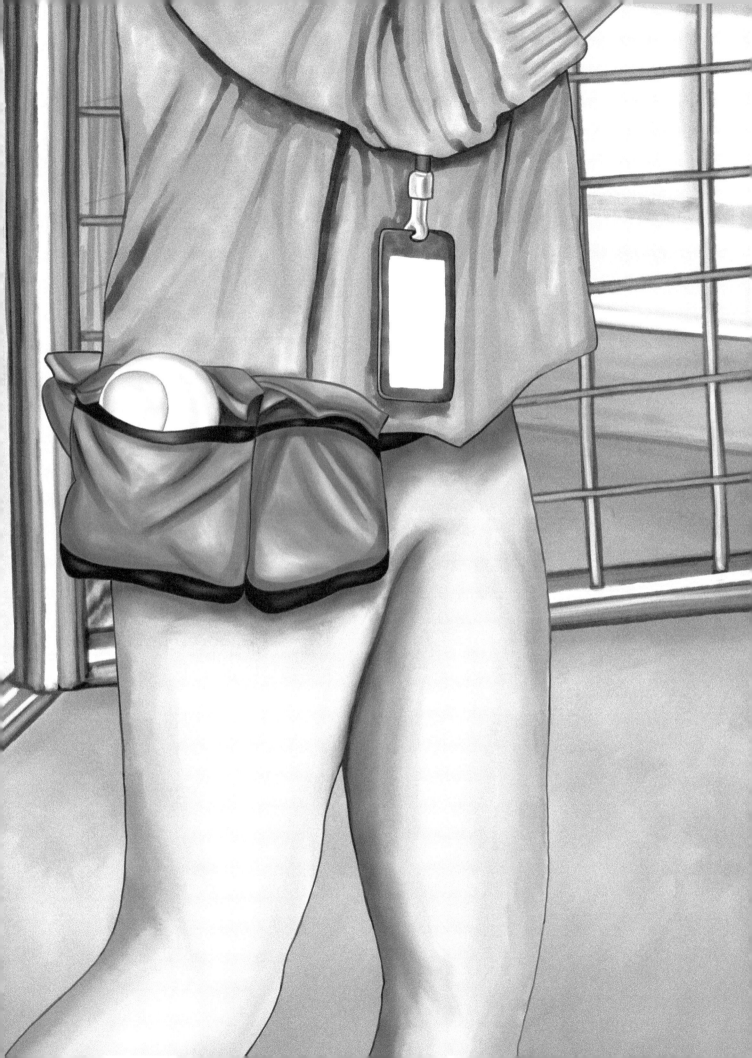

Jennie led her outside to a fenced area where Gabbi romped as much as she wanted without a leash.

When Jennie tossed the ball, Gabbi scooped it up and ran the entire yard, proudly carrying it in her mouth.

Several times over the next few weeks, they
continued to play together. Eventually Gabbi
learned not only to "fetch" but also to drop the
ball "on command."

When Jennie offered a yummy treat as a reward, Gabbi always gave her new friend a lick of gratitude.

Gabbi's gentleness and love surprised Jennie and warmed her heart. She realized no one had ever really trained this sweet dog or given her a chance to learn. It gave her an idea that just might help Gabbi find a way out of her lonely room and into a forever home.

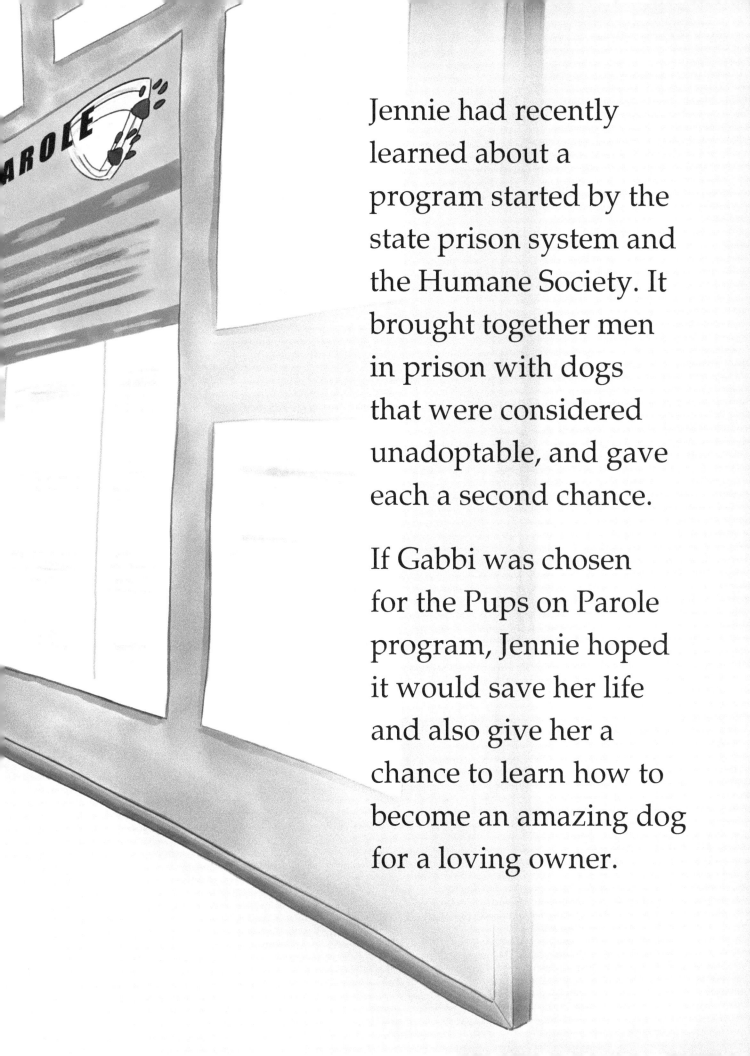

Jennie had recently learned about a program started by the state prison system and the Humane Society. It brought together men in prison with dogs that were considered unadoptable, and gave each a second chance.

If Gabbi was chosen for the Pups on Parole program, Jennie hoped it would save her life and also give her a chance to learn how to become an amazing dog for a loving owner.

Across town, a prisoner named Ben was experiencing many of the same sad and lonely feelings as Gabbi. He knew he had made a mistake… a bad one. Anger had caused him to harm someone, but that one action wasn't who he was.

Every day, he faced a world full of people who judged him. The more others judged him and believed him to be a "bad person," the more he started to believe it himself. That made him extremely sad. He desperately wanted to show the kindness deep in his heart.

Ben sat on the lower bunk bed in his cell and pushed himself back against the wall. He hadn't eaten for days. He didn't feel like joining any activities or talking to people in the yard. He didn't feel like getting up in the morning, and slept as much as he could during the day.

Ben, like Gabbi, wanted to be invisible.

One morning, a poster in the prison hallway caught Ben's attention. It announced a new program called Pups on Parole. He loved the idea of working with a dog! The thought of possibly saving the life of even one animal made him feel a spark of hope.

The more Ben learned about the program, the more he wanted to be chosen as a trainer. He was determined to work very hard to prove he could do it. He took on little jobs around the prison and did them well. Then he took on bigger jobs and did them better than anyone else.

Step by step, he proved he was ready to take on the responsibility of working with another living being, a dog.

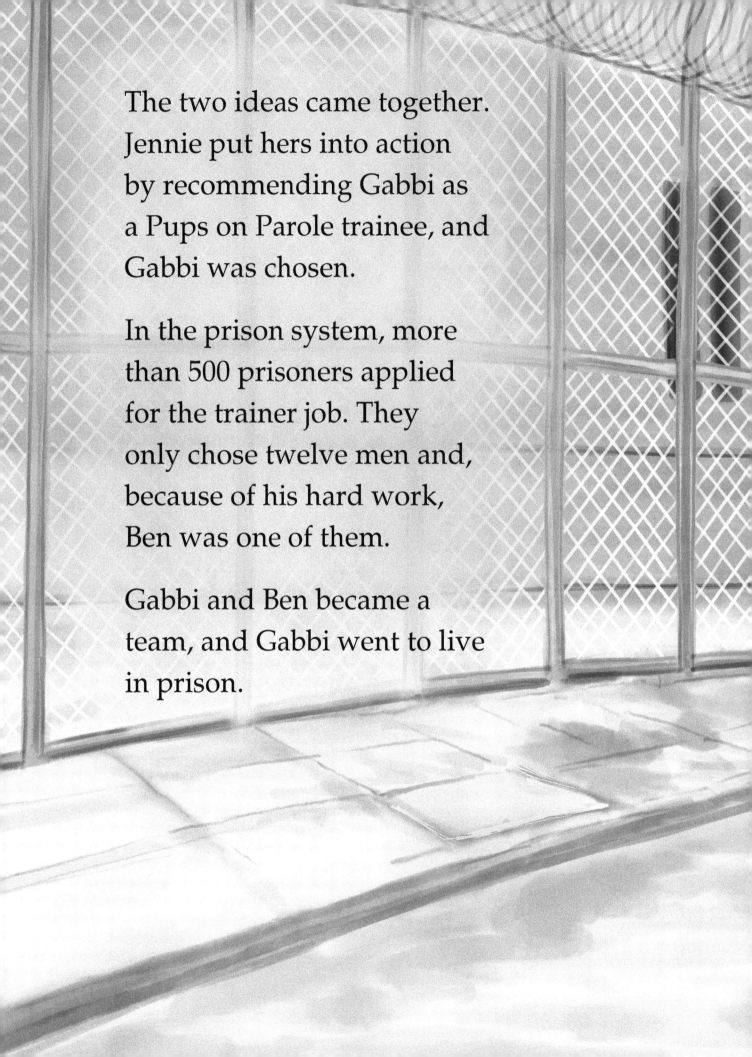

The two ideas came together.
Jennie put hers into action
by recommending Gabbi as
a Pups on Parole trainee, and
Gabbi was chosen.

In the prison system, more
than 500 prisoners applied
for the trainer job. They
only chose twelve men and,
because of his hard work,
Ben was one of them.

Gabbi and Ben became a
team, and Gabbi went to live
in prison.

While Gabbi liked being away from that lonely room, she was afraid she might do something to cause her to be taken back. But Ben showed her love from day one. It took a little time, but under his care while living together in the same "big cage," he soon noticed Gabbi changing from fearful to curious about what was going on around them.

He made it his mission to help her learn all the correct behaviors outside of the "bars." With that goal in mind, they got to work.

Every day, Ben journaled about Gabbi's progress and quick mind. She learned to open the yard gate herself by watching the prison staff open it each morning. She pushed the handle with her nose, which made him laugh.

It amazed him how fast she learned by observing.

Ben worked with her to learn all the commands she needed to graduate from Pups on Parole. He taught her the meaning and actions for "sit," "come," and "stay."

Gabbi sailed through the training with ease. Her intelligence, love of praise and treats, and growing faith in Ben made her an excellent student.

Each successful step of training made Ben proud. He couldn't wait to share stories about her accomplishments, and show others what she could do.

When Gabbi learned to "shake hands" or do a "high five," she would look into Ben's eyes with something he had never experienced before… unconditional love.

Ben soon recognized Gabbi was learning something you can't teach with a training manual. She was learning to trust and love. It came from his caring responses and interactions with her over time, every day. It was the most important thing she could learn, the thing that would help her most in finding a forever home. Even if she didn't respond well at first, she was praised for being a "good dog."

Their mutual love taught them that they may need to change a behavior here or there, but their hearts were always "good."

Ben also realized a change in himself. His confidence grew. He began to replace his many thoughts about being bad with thoughts about the good he was doing.

He chose to leave his past in the past, and began to see his future filled with much more love and patience, joy and hope.

Pups on Parole graduation day arrived. Gabbi and Ben showed everyone who attended what they had accomplished as a team.

Jennie came to the ceremony. Seeing Gabbi's progress, such pride filled her heart she could barely hold back tears. The time had come to post this wonderful dog's picture on the Humane Society website to let the world know she was ready for a forever home.

Graduation, though a bit sad, also brought Gabbi confidence and hope. Ben and she had grown in many ways through a relationship which taught her so much more than understanding basic commands. The relationship had caused a change of heart in each of them.

It was time to leave the past behind and move forward.

Once again, Gabbi found herself back in the lonely room. Luckily, her confusion at returning there did not last long, because Jennie had a wonderful surprise waiting for her.

A family looking for "just the right dog" found Gabbi's picture and story on the Humane Society website. They wanted her. Not only did they want just the right dog, they knew *she* was the dog, and asked for her by name.

All the way to her new home,
the family told Gabbi over and
over, "You are the perfect dog
for us. You are just the right
dog for our family. You are
such a good dog!"

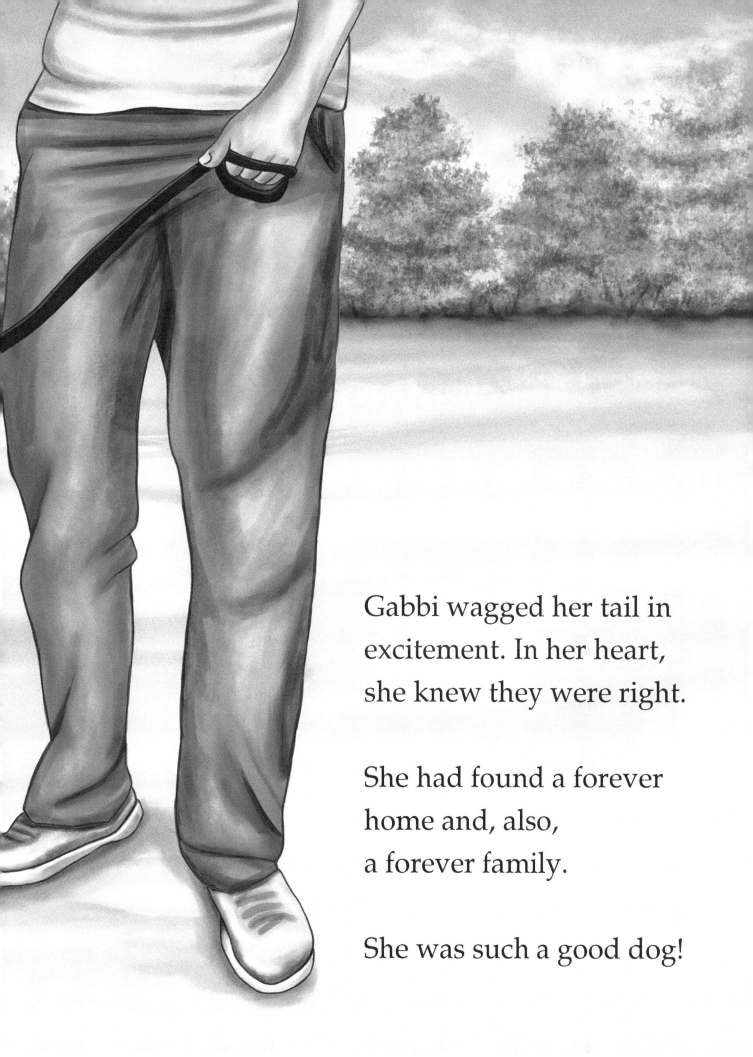

Gabbi wagged her tail in
excitement. In her heart,
she knew they were right.

She had found a forever
home and, also,
a forever family.

She was such a good dog!

Pups on Parole Background

The Pups on Parole Program was originally founded in 2002 through a partnership between the Nevada Humane Society and the Nevada Department of Corrections. The first eight dogs arrived at Nevada State Prison in Carson City, under the guidance of Director Jackie Crawford and Warden Michael Budge, in August 2002. The program's main objective was to give dogs that had behavioral issues and failed adoptions a second chance by receiving training to help them through behavioral modification. It also served as a second chance for many of the prisoners who became trainers.

In the 2010–2012 time frame, due to the closing of the Nevada State Prison, the dogs and prisoners were moved to Warm Springs Correctional Institute under Warden Greg Smith who promoted the continuation of the program. For a period of time, Carson City Animal Services also worked with the dogs and prisoners.

There are several other similar programs in both men's and women's prisons across the country.

This particular story, told in *Eye to Eye, Heart to Heart*, is a true account of a real dog, Gabbi, and a real prisoner, whose actual name is unknown, that took place in Warm Springs Correctional Center near Carson City, Nevada, in the 2015–2016 time frame.

A Prison Doctor's Perspective on the Pups on Parole Program in the Nevada Department of Corrections

In 2002, halfway through my thirty-year career as a prison doctor, the Nevada Department of Corrections (NDOC) started Pups on Parole, which won the hearts and minds of individuals on both sides of the fence line. As a prison doctor, I saw the violence decrease on the prison yard, along with racial tensions.

What affected me most though, was the positive effect it had on the inmates, the ones selected to be taught to be trainers of dogs considered unadoptable by the Humane Society. Those dogs were abused, neglected, abandoned, and not socialized. Dogs that needed love, understanding, intensive training, and deserved a second chance. Though the Humane Society believed in such training, it didn't have the resources and the people who could spend seven days a week, twenty-four hours a day for months, to give that type of care.

That all changed when Pups on Parole started at Nevada State Prison in Cell Block 5, once known as Death Row. I saw hardened men who had been in prison for twenty years, tear up with gratitude when they told me about the dog they were training, and what they felt when they could pet and feed the dog and look into eyes that did not judge them.

I saw inmates who walked straighter, smiled more, and didn't access medical and psych services as much as they had in the past. I also saw less fighting and less trauma for me to deal with.

It was a win-win situation. The inmates and the dogs both received a second chance to become their best selves, and the prison and society were better off for it.

—Karen Gedney, M.D., author of *30 Years Behind Bars*

Note from a Former Prisoner and Pups on Parole Trainer

My time in the Pups on Parole program was very rewarding. Even though our objective was to help and train dogs with certain issues that kept them from being adopted, they also helped in bringing back a little bit of the sanity you lose when you go to prison. I spent twenty-two years in prison, and the only place you could find relative peace was within your own mind sometimes. You sure didn't want to expose your feelings to other inmates for fear of being looked at as weak.

When the dog program was introduced I was lucky enough to become a member. I remember my first couple dogs were hard cases, kinda like me. LOL. We were told, for some of these dogs, this was their last chance. Being in the position of being told those same very words, it really hit home.

Here is this dog that didn't do anything wrong, but was never given proper training or love by anyone. So you make it your mission to save this animal and do whatever it takes to train them and give them the attention they deserve.

When they leave, it can be pretty sad because of the attachment that has been created. But what is more rewarding is when you find out they have been adopted and gone to a good family, and they do well. There are a lot of parallels to what the dog goes through and what somebody incarcerated goes through. For me, the dog program brought a level of happiness back into my life. It gave me more hope. It allowed me to let my guard down and show true emotion and love towards these animals and even in my own life. It taught me a lot of patience.

In general, I feel I came out of that place a better man because of the things I got to learn and experience directly from that program. So, yes, I helped save plenty of good dogs while a trainer in the program, but the dogs I trained also helped save me, too, teaching me so many things along the way that have been so beneficial.

—Robert Reed, former Pups on Parole trainer, Nevada Department of Corrections

A Note from the Author to Parents, Teachers, Foster Parents, and Caregivers

This story was written totally from the heart. Our dog, Gabbi, has been a source of much love and joy since we adopted each other in April of 2016. At the time of that mutual adoption, she was only a year-and-a-half old, and she exhibited many of the fresh raw fears and behaviors associated with an abused and neglected dog. Even one of us holding a newspaper made her cower into a corner. She indeed needed a lot of love in order to trust us, but she did, little by little, day by day.

She quickly inched her way into our hearts and souls, and settled in for the ride. We were not experienced dog owners, and to bring this sassy girl into our lives was indeed a challenge. Just like raising children, we didn't do everything correctly the first time out. We, unfortunately, learned through trial and error.

To continue making this story a truthful tale, it is only fair to remind all readers that the adoption was not the end of the story. It was just the beginning. It was sometimes very challenging to know the right thing to do. On rare occasions, Gabbi would act out as a way of protecting her newfound family… or just to be in control of a situation she had never had control of before. The more she loved us, the more she wanted to protect us which, at times, could create difficult situations.

I wrote this book to give us all hope that unconditional love can help erase emotional pain. But I also wrote it as a reminder that every living being needs love and kindness, especially during "formative" years. Harsh, mean-intentioned words and violence hurt and leave emotional and physical scars that take years and years—if ever—to fade away.

There will be children who hear or read this book who may have experienced or are experiencing many of the same feelings as Gabbi and Ben. The story is intended to provide an opportunity to let them share their feelings, to be listened to, to participate in a heartfelt discussion, and help them know how much they matter.

I also hope, after reading this book, you will step back and take a deep breath when you are angry with a child, an animal, or with another person. Strive to become aware of your feelings, and modify the words you say or actions you take. *Stop. Breathe. Say or do nothing* until you can find a "kinder way" to express how you are feeling. If you overcome an angry response even once, this book will have served its purpose.

About Gabbi

Gabbi is a real dog, a "rescue dog" from the Pups on Parole program. After having her DNA tested, we found her to be part German shepherd and part pit bull. We have tried to tell her story as accurately as possible from history shared with us by the Humane  Society and prisoner program representatives. Whatever her biological DNA, her soul is one full of love.

One day, while taking her for a walk, she saw an elderly woman on the other side of the road. As if planned, Gabbi walked slowly toward the woman who, in turn, had slowly started walking toward her. Gabbi rubbed her head against the woman's leg as the woman leaned over to pet our dog's neck and head. The exchange of love was moving.

The woman explained how her dog had recently passed and, due to her declining health, was unable to take care of a new dog. Somehow, Gabbi sensed the need for love and took it upon herself to share hers with this lady.

I recognized then, as I had many times before, Gabbi's ability to "read" a person's soul immediately. She sensed hostility and anger but, most often, she felt a person's need for a gentle touch of compassion. Gabbi knows who she loves and who she doesn't trust… from across a street or a room. Maybe Gabbi's past of being abused heightened her sense of "feeling" the people around her.

Overcoming her fears and protectiveness has been a challenge, but we are grateful to this day that Gabbi came into our lives in April of 2016 and became our four legged "fur baby."

About the Illustrator

Joan Zander Millard grew up near the Ice Age Trail, located in southcentral Wisconsin. The trail highlights the state's many lakes, river valleys, gently rolling hills and ridges, carved out by the massive glacier that covered most of North America during the Ice Age. At an early age, she was able to explore the trail and its many wonders during family outings, where she developed a love of her natural surroundings and the animals that roam there. This helped stoke an interest in art, which began her lifelong passion for drawing, especially natural scenery and animals.

Joan's professional career has always drawn upon her artistic background, whether she was teaching drawing and design fundamentals, working for one of the largest advertising agencies in Madison for clients such as Ray-O-Vac and Oscar Mayer, designing online learning tutorials, or managing commissioned illustration work.

Joan and her husband built a beautiful house on the family homestead, and she continues to be artistically inspired by the local natural surroundings. They share their rural home with their two sons and many pets.

About the Author

Pamela "Pam" Pech—considered a thought leader, workshop creator, and discussion facilitator—reads avidly and frequently incorporates books into her self-awareness projects for both adults and children.

A retiree from corporate America as a business executive, and a former educator and entrepreneur, Pam now follows her full-time passion: creating programs and facilitating discussions which promote self-understanding and sense of purpose.

Pam's teaching experience ranges from preschool through junior high and adult education. She is a Certified SoulCollage® Facilitator, and uses that and her love of books to launch many group discussions.

Her "discovery of Self®" programs are created out of a desire to bring people together through conversation. Not only do these discussions illustrate the power of listening to one another, but also how the sharing of ideas brings about individual and collective discovery of purpose. She has conducted numerous women's leadership workshops under Essential Leadership, and is currently working on a "Warriorship" Training program, based on the concept of the Shambhala warrior. It encompasses individual wisdom as the gift of service to the world—strongly tied to discovery of Self®.

A mom of two grown children and a grandma of four, Pam resides between Reno and Lake Tahoe with Gary, her husband of thirty-six years, and, of course, Gabbi.

Lightning Source UK Ltd.
Milton Keynes UK
UKHW050250010223
416284UK00014B/118